This Sporting Life

This Sporting Life

Ken Pyne

The Kingswood Press

The Kingswood Press
an imprint of William Heinemann Ltd.
10 Upper Grosvenor Street, London W1X 9PA
LONDON   MELBOURNE
JOHANNESBURG   AUCKLAND

Text and illustrations copyright © 1986 Ken Pyne

First published 1986

Printed in Great Britain by
Redwood Burn Ltd, Trowbridge, Wiltshire

0 434 98098 6

Dear Derek, Margot & Louise,

I did give serious thought to your suggestion of an acknowledgement in the book to my wife but I've decided against it — Mainly, I think, because I'm not married.

All the best,

Ken.

DEDICATED TO THE UNKNOWN ALL-ROUNDER

"You know something? I don't think I've the heart to throw it back."

"I'm part of a cultural exchange with Hull Kingston Rovers."

"I'm sorry, Nigel, we've been roller skating for two years now and I've come to the conclusion that our relationship is purely physical."

"We're pot-holers."

"He's never really recovered his form since Elvis died."

"It was a nice, quiet area until they turned the Church Hall into a Trampolining Club."

"Who the hell do you think they are? They're my sponsors!"

"Rumour has it they've been pumping his brain full of anabolic steroids."

"What do I think it is that has made me this country's greatest water ski exponent?
I think it's the fact that I can't swim."

"In his day he was a Bondi legend."

"I'll tell you the only reason mine plays the stupid game – so everybody can see
he earns over £100,000 a year!"

"What do you mean 'Drowning him was cold-blooded murder'? It was a professional foul!"

"I take it that this is your first game of water polo."

"You realize, of course, that the *real* title
we're playing for is that of 'the poor man's Steve Davis'"

"Talk about confident!"

"I suppose if they do ban all this we could always become Chelsea supporters."

"Look! I'm the map reader here and if I say this is the Guildford Bypass then this *is* the Guildford Bypass!"

"As you are new to the modern pentathlon let me explain – it's true you will be required to ride, fence, shoot, swim and run but not all on the same day!"

"I believe he took it up in his early days, when he preached amongst Hell's Angels."

"I've spotted his weakness. He's an insecure man who likes to relieve his deep-rooted feelings of inadequacy by punching me in the face."

"I was wondering if occasionally – just occasionally – instead of bridge parties we could celebrate our middle class status with an orgy."

"I've been worried about my game lately — my last match only attracted
8.6 million viewers."

"Gerald has refused to let his agoraphobia interfere with his passion for small game shooting."

"But they can't *all* be lost! This is the National Orienteering Championship!"

"Despite his enthusiasm I often think he doesn't get all that he could out of the sport."

"I feel the sport has lost a lot of its dignity – there was a time when they were quite content just to give a 'V' sign."

"I've only come to get a broken leg so I can go back and tell everybody in my
local wine bar that I did it skiing."

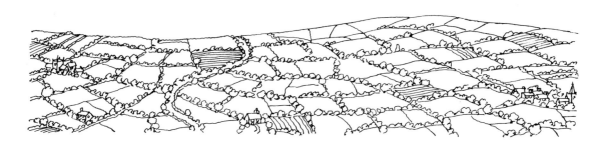

"Honestly, Gerald, you have no idea how much I appreciate you at last bringing
me on one of your sky-diving weekends."

"I don't know, this just hasn't been as much fun since we lost the empire."

"Good God! He's right! There is nothing in the rules against it."

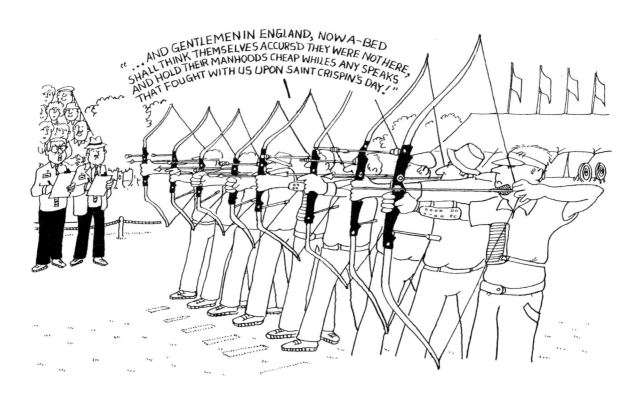

"There's always one!"

"For Heaven's sake, mother, I'm old enough to go out on my own now!"

"Good grief! If it's one thing I can't stand it's middle aged Torvill and Deans!"

"Have you chaps by any chance seen any other boats in the Chichester-Bournemouth single-handed race pass by this way?"

"It's the beachbum's menopause – too old to go surfing and too young to go sailing."

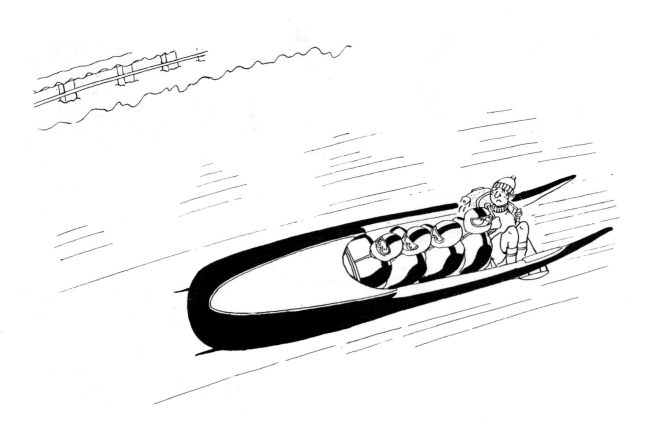

"We don't normally stop to give lifts you know."

"Neither of them can play particularly well but they're both *great* competitors."

"I'm not sure – there was a chappie from Nanking in the early sixties who also had a pretty devilish spin serve…"

"He's everything a great player should be – fast, strong, intelligent, determined, psychopathic…"

"Just as I suspected, Barstow! You're no darts champion!"

"All right! All right! – *I'll* be Basil Rathbone and *you* can be Errol Flynn!"

"His handicap is that he doesn't realize that he should let his boss win."

"No, my parents don't understand me either. They made me take this up to keep me away from drugs, glue-sniffing and mugging old ladies when all I wanted to do was play chess."

"It's round the clock training for our holidays. Gordon is determined we're going to be the best volleyball team on the beach at Torremolinos."

"I don't know what I'm doing here, either! I set off this morning intending to go to my job at the glue factory in Rochdale."

"Here we go again! To get the cameras on him he resorts to doing impressions!"

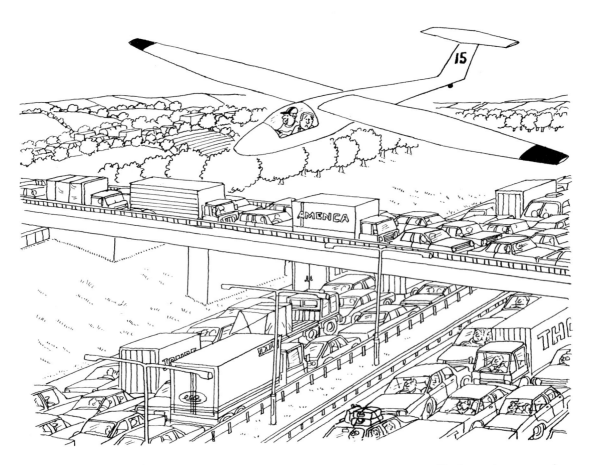

"Actually, this is the only reason I come gliding – I find flying over traffic jams does wonders for my inferiority complex."

"I don't know, Brian, this just isn't as much fun as it used to be."

"What was it that made me fall in love with cricket? The realization that there's sod all else to do on Sunday afternoons."

"On reflection, sitting in the office getting overweight and being terrified of approaching middle age isn't so bad after all…"

"And a sad loss to curling."

"I thought so! Wiggins of 4C!"

"I know she's an Olympic diving gold medallist but now she's just showing off!"

"Why must I be the only one with a wife who insists on coming stock car racing with him?"

"It's the marathon."

"He never misses a chance to let everybody know that he's also a figure skating champion."

"I hear he's been making a fool of himself over some woman."

"Stop the game! His glass eye has fallen out again!"

"Apparently, his great great grandfather on his mother's side was Greek."

"Actually, I only took up speedway so I'd have something to put on my computer dating card – I was rather hoping it would make me appear virile."

"If you ask me, the drugs tests at these games have been far from adequate!"

"What depresses me about these Sunday morning games is that they're the most enjoyable thing in my life."

"That's the trouble with this bloody game! No chance to thrash the Poms at it!"

"Listen, limey, you once civilized your empire with cricket – now we're going to civilize ours with baseball!"

"...and this is Eddie – the dwarf of the team."

"No matter how many times I win it never compensates for always coming last in the rat race."

"You know, I've always been grateful to Rugby League for giving me an escape from a life of dirt and grime down the pit."

"Apparently he's the all-army champion of South America."

"It's about time Walton made his mind up once and for all! It's either lacrosse or butterfly collecting!"

"Isn't it a sad fact of sporting life that those so rich in enthusiasm are so often the poorest in talent?"

"I tell you, I'm really on my uppers – I haven't been bribed in weeks."

"Yes, he's a good long jumper but I often think his lack of technique lets him down."

"He got the height but he didn't get the distance."

"It's not actually the *playing* of the game that's retaliation against my husband's Sunday morning football – it's the drinking of ten pints in the pub afterwards."

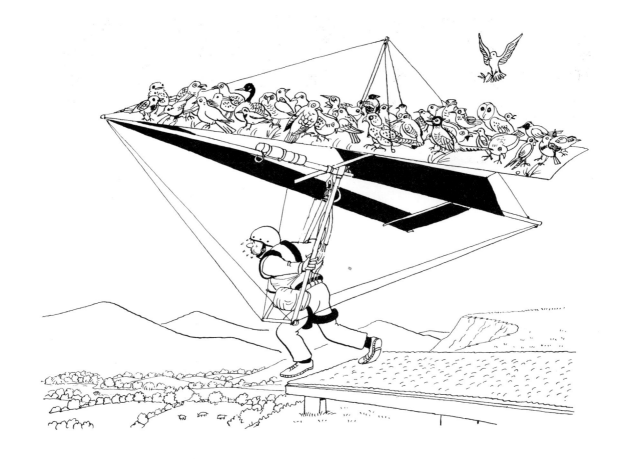

"To be honest, I only took this up after years of having no luck hanging around gay bars."

"You mean we *all* think badminton's a
bloody boring game and we'd all prefer
to spend our evenings in the pub?"

"Tragic, yes, but unquestionably an Olympic javelin record."